Flea Treat

Jan Burchett and Sara Vogler
Illustrated by Trevor Dunton

Chapters

			Page
	**Chapter 1**	The Fleas	3
	Chapter 2	The Treat	7
	Chapter 3	The Plan	12
	Chapter 4	The Escape	20

Chapter 1
The Fleas

Once there was a dog who had no home. She had no family and no name. But she did have something. She had fleas.

She had lots of fleas. The fleas had lived on the dog for a long time. Old Seth was the oldest flea. Only he could remember living anywhere else. "This is the best home I've ever had!" he always told the other fleas.

The fleas had a happy life on their dog. They laughed, they played and they slept. When they were hungry, they had a bite to eat. They bit the dog. When they bit the dog, the dog would scratch. When the dog scratched, people would say, "Go away, you horrible dog. You have fleas."

Tim, Tom and Tammy were the youngest fleas.
They loved climbing up to the very top of the dog's
head. From there, they could see what was going on
in the outside world. But one day, they looked out
and saw that something was very wrong. They were
not outside any more!

Chapter 2
The Treat

Tim, Tom and Tammy could see that their dog was in a house! A little girl was patting the dog. She almost squashed Tim!

"Hello, doggy," the girl said. "This is your new home. And I will call you Scrap."

A man was peering at the dog. "And we'll take you to the vet," he said. "She'll treat your fleas!"

"The vet's going to treat us!" cried Tim.

"What's a vet?" asked Tom.

"I don't know," said Tammy, "but it's going to give us a treat."

"What do you think the treat will be?" Tim asked the other fleas.

"Maybe we're going to the flea circus!" shouted Tom.

"Let's go and tell the others!" said Tammy.

Tim, Tom and Tammy told the other fleas about their dog's new home — and all about the treat. The fleas shouted and waved their legs in the air.

"But where's Old Seth?" asked Tammy suddenly. "We must tell him too."

8

All the fleas went to see Old Seth. "The vet's going to give us a treat!" shouted Tim.

"Maybe we're going to the zoo!" cried Tom.

But Old Seth didn't shout or wave his legs in the air. Instead he frowned and shook his head. "I remember vets," he said. "Vets don't like fleas. A treat must be something bad."

Old Seth got his dictionary. He looked up the word *treat.* "*Treat,*" he read. "To do something nice for someone."

"Told you!" said Tim.

"Maybe the vet will take us to a fair!" cried Tom.

"Wait a minute," said Old Seth. "*Treat* means something else too. To treat a dog's fleas is to get rid of them!"

Chapter 3
The Plan

"That's not what I call a treat," cried Tim.

"What are we going to do?" the other fleas asked Old Seth.

"We must find a new dog to live on," said Old Seth.

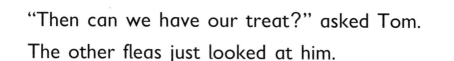

"Then can we have our treat?" asked Tom.

The other fleas just looked at him.

"Come on," said Old Seth. "There's no time to lose.
We must jump off our dog."

"Jump?" asked the other fleas. "How do we jump?"

"All fleas can jump," said Old Seth.

"We can't!" shouted the other fleas.

"Watch me," said Old Seth. "I'll show you how to jump. I will jump as high as a horse!" Old Seth tried to jump as high as a horse. But he couldn't even jump as high as a spider's knee!

The other fleas tried to jump too. But they couldn't even jump as high as an ant's knee! The fleas had lived on their dog for so long that they couldn't remember how to jump!

Then the girl and the man came back. The girl patted Scrap's head and put a hair band in her hair. She almost squashed Tim.

"Watch it!" Tim shouted to the girl.

Then the man said, "Time to go to the vet, Scrap."

"Yippee!" cried Tom. "Time for our treat!"

"Help!" shouted the other fleas. "We're going to die!"

"We need another plan," said Old Seth, scratching his head.

"I've got a plan," said Tim. "Let's stay here and hide."

Old Seth shook his head. "No, the vet will find us," he said.

"I've got a plan," said Tom. "Let's climb off our dog."

"The dog is walking," said Old Seth. "We can't climb off while she's walking. We'll fall!"

"I've got a plan," said Tammy. "Let's fly off our dog!"

"Fleas can't fly," said Old Seth.

"*We* can," said Tammy. "Come with me, fleas!" She led the fleas to the top of the dog's head. She pointed to the hair band in the dog's hair. "This band will help us fly," Tammy said.

"How can that help us fly?" asked Old Seth.

"Watch!" said Tammy with a grin.

Tammy leaned on the hair band. She pushed back hard. Then she let go. The band pinged her into the air.

"She flew!" shouted the other fleas. Then Tammy fell back down on the dog.

"If we all push on the band together, we will fly a long way," she said.

"Is this our treat?" asked Tom.

"No," said Tammy. "This is how we escape!"

Chapter 4
The Escape

Just then, Scrap got to the vet's door.

"Help!" cried the fleas. "We're going to die!"

"Quick! Get in the hair band!" shouted Tammy.

All the fleas got in the hair band. They pushed back hard with their legs and let go. They hurtled through the air.

"Whee!" shouted the fleas. "We're flying! We've escaped!"

Then the fleas were falling!
"Help!" shouted the fleas. "We're falling!"

The fleas landed on something warm and fluffy. "Where are we?" asked Tim.

Old Seth had a look around. "We're on a new dog," he said. He gave the dog a little bite. "Not bad!" he told the other fleas.

"Yippee!" shouted Tim, Tom and Tammy. "We have found a new home!"

"Yippee!" shouted the other fleas.

"Can we have our treat now?" asked Tom.

"Sorry, Tom," said Old Seth, shaking his head.
"I don't think there is going to be a treat."

But Old Seth was wrong. The fleas got their treat
after all!